In Search Of The Ultimate Practice

Developing, Maintaining, and Enjoying a
Patient-Centered Dental Practice

by
William G. Dickerson, DDS

For further information: Southwest Seminars
4011 Meadows Lane, Suite 101, Las Vegas, Nevada 89107
(702) 878-1977

Dedication

This book is dedicated to all the dentists who are no longer with us, but spent their lives teaching others how to be more successful while maintaining a quality based practice. To all the Pankeys, Barkleys, and Wirths.... Thank you!

It is also dedicated to my son, Dylan, whose time with his father has been altered by my "mission."

FOREWARD
by
Walter Hailey

Having built several companies over the last forty years, I don't know much about cosmetic dentistry, but I do know a lot about people, persuasion and marketing. Spend a half-century watching businesses and dollars and cents go 'round, as I have, and you start seeing remakes of the same old stories. Dentistry is starting to look a lot like grocery retailing in the 1950s and 60s.

My first multi-million-dollar deals involved marketing insurance to grocers, a clientele I got to know very well selling flour, my first job after college. In the decades after World War II the whole grocery business hollowed out. Medium-small independents were devastated by lower-pricing big chains.

These days huge gets even 'huger.' But, a certain kind of small grocer is also booming. Market-specific gourmet shops, with high-quality products and individualized service, do better than ever.

There's a difference, in principle, in how mass marketers and niche-specific businesses succeed. The first do it by selling products as commodities, competing primarily on price. The elite thrive by specializing and focusing on value, the sum total of everything exceptional about their products and services.

Industry after industry has lost its middle, leaving low-end and high. Some say the whole country is hollowing out.

But, no matter what happens, being the best, with an informed, loyal clientele who doesn't mind meeting your price, will always be a formula for business success. It's a formula for personal success, too. Target a market that you know and like, which fully understands and appreciates the value of what you offer, and you'll be doing what you want to do, with your favorite people. And, you'll be stress free.

Now that dentistry is hollowing out, the practitioner is faced with two basic choices. One is to become part of a chain structure, a PPO or HMO or capitation plan. If this is all you do to keep your operatory chair full, you're in commodity dentistry.

Commodity dentistry is great for the chain owner. But in most cases the dentist and his or her skills are the commodity -- and they're paying to sit on somebody else's shelf!

The alternative is to take total control of your practice's destiny, offering state-of-the-art care to people committed to their dental health. We're talking about gourmet dentistry. And, it's delicious. But no large scale outside entity is going to make this work for you.

In the four companies that I have started, built and taken public, there is a constant theme that has repeated itself over and over. It is a natural law that has not been violated since the beginning of time. Fifteen percent of your success will come from your technical and clinical ability and 85% will come from your ability to get people to want to do what you have determined that they need to do.

Last year, there was over thirty-one billion dollars worth of dentistry that was not done in America. Half the people don't have a "Happy Dental Home"....a place where they go on a regular basis to get ALL of their dental needs taken care of. Yet, 80% have some type of serious problem that a dentist and dental team could help cure. Add on to that the 80 million baby boomers that are starting to move into mid-life and are starting to realize the consequences of forty plus years of dental neglect. They have a primary objective, to look good and feel good. No one else can help them more to make their mouths to look and feel good than a dentist and his team. It is one of the single biggest marketing opportunities that I have ever seen.

Through our Dental "Boot Kamp" seminars, we have worked hard to help dentists and their teams overcome many obstacles in their minds that prevent them from reaching their full potential to take advantage of the great marketing opportunity that exists in dentistry.

The biggest obstacle is what we call 'Approval Addiction.' There is absolutely no reason why any professional should feel guilty or take responsibility for poor dental work done in the past by someone else or for neglect on the patient's part. A strong approval addiction or overwhelming need to be liked stands in the way of presenting total dentistry, of helping the patient understand everything that is available to them, and it stands in the way of being able to deliver total and comprehensive central care.

Another obstacle is the lack of understanding of the difference between leadership and management. Management is doing things right but leadership is doing the right things. There is nothing as powerful as a practice that is lead by a leader, a dentist, who has a 'Vivid Vision that Vibrates Violently' in the minds and hearts of everyone on the dental team. Once that is established, then everyone can concentrate on carrying out the management systems that have been put in place to make sure that each and every patient is provided with a quality care experience.

Ultimately, you can have the greatest clinical skills in the world, have a 'Vivid Vision' and great management systems, but if you can't market what you do with professionalism and class, you will struggle along with the huddled masses who have great ideas and skills..... but they are the only ones who know about it.

Back when there was more middle in the world than anything else, you could ignore marketing and survive by accident. All you had to be was pretty good, and pretty nice. The corner grocer used to get by like that too. But now he's as gone as Tyrannosaurus Rex.

Don't join him! Go out and do what you ought to do!

Pro-Actively Yours,

Walter Hailey

From The Author

A few years ago I wrote "The Exceptional Dental Practice." In it, I explored and explained the skills needed to enjoy a rewarding and successful professional life. Much to my pleasure, the book was extremely well received. Many people, however, told me that while it was the basis for great change in their office, it opened new questions for them. For instance, they wanted to know how to fine-tune the change they had begun and how to keep the momentum and excitement alive.

These queries prompted me to contemplate the steps it takes to develop a thriving high-end dental practice.

I almost quit dentistry in the late 1980s because of my disenchantment with our profession. I now love dentistry and feel it can be an extremely rewarding career. What I have examined here is how I evolved from one emotion to the other. What I discovered is that not only did my philosophy have to change, but that what was most important was to *keep that philosophy on track,* because, as Will Rogers said, 'Even if you're on the right track, you'll get run over if you just sit there.'

This book is an attempt to share with you the ideas I have put in use to keep customers satisfied and my rewards plenty.

Many of you will find an excuse for why this plan won't work for you. If I had a dollar for every time I have heard that comment, I would be a wealthy man. The truth is, these ideas will work for any office in any location. The more pertinent questions are these: Do you have the will and desire to implement these changes into your philosophy of practice? Do you have the vision to keep that philosophy on track?

Change is difficult for all of us, as it requires action or energy. It is certainly simpler to not do anything than to incorporate changes that may be difficult to implement. Fear of failure prevents many of us from changing, since you can't miss a shot you don't shoot. If statistics hold true, 80 percent of you will do nothing after reading this book, even though you may say you want to. Perhaps your team members' attitudes stifle the initiation of change. Perhaps your own inertia prevents it. There are myriad things that can prevent you from actually doing something constructive -- if you let them.

You will find it useful to read -- or reread -- "The Exceptional Dental Practice," first. Then, read this book. Afterwards, map out a plan and have a team meeting, sharing your plan with the other team members. Place the items in the order in which you want them accomplished. If you find yourself getting behind, it's because you have let it happen. Read the book again and hopefully it will ignite the desire you once had. Don't let the examples in this book be your only guide, but use this book as a springboard to further investigate the practice of improving ideas. Read business literature that has nothing to do with dentistry, yet may contain principles that can be applied to a dental practice.

I used to think that I wanted no part of the business aspect of dentistry and only wanted to come in and work IN the practice, not ON it. I was wrong. I have enjoyed developing and building a successful business more than anything. The challenge is what keeps you going. Remember, the reward of life is not the end result, but the *journey*. I will *continue* to search for the ultimate practice. I am constantly trying to reach my goals. When I reach them, I will set new ones.

Abraham Lincoln said, "Man is about as happy as he makes up his mind to be." If you are unhappy with your practice, do something about it. If you keep doing it the same way, your going to keep getting the same results. Good luck with your journey. And remember: Enjoy the process!

William G. Dickerson, DDS
Las Vegas, Nevada
1995

Table of Contents

Chapter One

The First Business Principle
The Nickel and Dime Mentality

Plateau (pla-toe) -- *A roughly level section in a graph (e.g. of progress in production, showing little or no advance).*

Dr. Plateau read "The Exceptional Dental Practice," and as a result made some changes in his practice. These changes had an initial effect on his practice, but the enthusiasm had waned two years later. It was the same with his team. He found the service that they initially worked so hard to provide had somewhat diminished and was not drawing the same appreciation from their patients.

Dr. Excel, the subject and inspiration of the first book, happened to live in a nearby town. Dr. Plateau decided that there must be more to the story than was reported in the book. He decided to give Dr. Excel a call and see if he had some words of wisdom that would help get him past the blockage that was preventing his growth.

"Dr. Excel's office. Karen speaking. May I help you?" asked a pleasant sounding voice through the telephone line.

"Yes, this is Dr. Plateau, may I speak to Dr. Excel?"

"Are you a newsletter subscriber?" asked Karen automatically.

"Well, no," Dr. Plateau answered apologetically, "but I was planning on it."

Karen had heard that line before, and while she felt uncomfortable doing so, she explained that due to the number of calls the practice received, the team at Dr. Excel's office had made a decision allowing the doctor to only talk to those who were newsletter subscribers.

She further explained that since publication, Dr. Excel had become extremely busy speaking to groups about his philosophy and clinical skills and had started the newsletter to keep his colleagues informed of changes and pertinent information. She said that the doctor was finding it hard to devote the time to his practice due to the demand for his time and that the volume of calls he received had to be contained.

"The truth is that most of the questions people ask are in the past issues of the newsletter," she said. "Would you like to be placed on the mailing list?"

At that moment, Dr. Excel walked by and overheard the conversation.

"Karen, let me talk to him. I'll go to my office. I have a few minutes," he said, looking at his watch.

"It's your lucky day," said Karen to Dr. Plateau.

While on hold, Dr. Plateau heard a message about the procedures that are performed in Dr. Excel's office. He thought how informative that was and certainly how much better it was for patients to hear a message about the practice than some radio commercial that is targeted at their discretionary dollar.

"Hello," Dr. Excel said enthusiastically. "This is Will Excel. What can I do for you?"

"Hi Will, I'm sorry to bother you. I read your book and I have been planning on getting your newsletter for some time, I just never got around to it," Dr. Plateau said sheepishly. "This is Evan Plateau. I am a dentist in Mt. Hicktown and wanted to ask you some questions."

"I want to ask you a question first" declared Will. "What prevented you from subscribing to the newsletter?" Without pausing to allow Evan to answer, Will continued. "Always keep in mind *the first business principle*. You have to spend money to make money!"

Evan just listened as Will continued.

"Why is it that some people I speak to and who read what I put into print, can make changes that improve their practice and ultimately their life? Why is it that others, given the same information, are unable, or unwilling, to make the necessary changes that will lead to success?"

"Well, I don't know..." stammered Dr. Plateau.

Dr. Excel plunged ahead. "Why is it that dentists who are given the opportunity to read and hear about these principles, choose not to and don't believe it will work in their lives. Do they think the investment is too much? If I knew the answer to those questions, I would be a very, very rich man!

"Why doesn't everyone listen? Why do I not get through to everyone? If you could shed some light on this, please let me know."

There was silence on the line.

"I am not saying I have all the answers," said Dr. Excel. "Far from it. But it's frustrating knowing that I know something that could help a person and they choose not to hear it."

"I don't think I know," said Evan, honestly, "Maybe it's because we are so inundated with information and offers that we have trouble deciding what to purchase."

"Dentists are really a funny lot and I was exactly like most dentists 7 or 8 years ago," said Will, apparently ignoring Evan. "I couldn't see the forest through the trees and, like most dentists, I was a terrible businessman. I didn't understand that I had to spend money to make money. That philosophy has a negative effect on a practice."

"What happened?" asked Evan.

"Omer Reed had a dramatic effect on my life. Incredibly, I almost didn't attend his weekend session myself, because of the cost of his program. I can tell you with great certainty that if I hadn't overcome this nickel and dime mentality, I would not be practicing dentistry today.

"I am not even sure what his weekend program costs now -- possibly $1300, or so -- and I can't even tell you anything specific that I got out of it, except a philosophical change."

"A philosophical change?" asked Evan, skeptically.

"Yes. Was it worth it? One year later, I was netting three times what I had been before attending his program. I'd say it was worth it!"

"I guess it was!" responded Evan, amazed.

"The fact is that 80% of dentists make no effort to educate themselves to new ways of doing business. Here's a good example. Last week, a doctor called who had attended one of my seminars *two years ago.* He explained to Emma, my treatment coordinator, that he was having sensitivity problems on 50% of the restorations he placed."

(Dr. Excel has also lectured on clinical techniques concerning esthetic dentistry.)

"Emma very nicely explained why I can't come to the phone for everyone who calls -- if I did I would never have time to practice dentistry -- and asked if he subscribed to the newsletter, explaining that the problem was probably covered in previous issues. He not only said that he wasn't interested in the newsletter, but that the sensitivity issue should have been covered in the seminar -- which it was --

meaning, he either forgot or hadn't paid attention at the time.

"Can you logically tell me why this doctor, who was having problems costing him several thousands of dollars in remakes, not to mention the inestimable loss of confidence in him with his patients, was too cheap to spend $62 a year to keep current with a procedure in which he is obviously interested?"

"He's an idiot?" replied Dr. Plateau, laughing.

"It might be okay, if it weren't that he's the norm," said Will, chuckling. "It happens all the time that dentists who have attended a past seminar will approach me at some later meeting and ask questions about techniques they are having trouble with, and the techniques will be those I have covered in the newsletter. And I find out they have chosen not to subscribe. The failures they were experiencing cost them far more than the dollar and change a week they could have spent on keeping up to date.

"Another dentist came up to me recently at the conclusion of a seminar. She was all excited and wanted to know more about my philosophy of running a practice and I told her the *best* thing she could do was read the book, "The Exceptional Dental Practice," and handed her a copy. She flipped through the pages and decided not to buy it. How could she have seen the value in the information in that short time she perused the book? Was the cost a factor?"

"Well, I..." Evan started to say something, but was interrupted by Will.

"It could have dramatically increased her income, or so I have been told by those who have read it," said Dr. Excel. "And yet she chose not to buy it."

"It sure helped me," said Evan, quickly.

"Good for you," said Will. "Don't nickel and dime your practice into mediocrity. As any *good* business person knows, you need to invest in your practice to keep it thriving. It's not enough to just keep the doors open, you need to make investments into new capital and equipment that enable you to provide superior service. I'm not telling you to jump on every new gadget that comes around -- I certainly don't do that -- but check out it's *return on it's investment.* If it will make you more money, make life easier, or make dentistry more fun, then I say go for it.

"If it's less than a hundred dollars, what do you have to lose? You should read "REALITY," "The Profitable Dentist," "The 21st Century Practice," or any other publication you even *think* may help you. You can't have too much information and if you only get one good idea a year from any of these publications, it was worth the price. Think about it!

"Thanks for letting me vent my frustrations," said Will.

"You bet," said Evan. As he waited for Dr. Excel to start talking again, he thought of how many times he had opted not to make a small investment that might have reaped larger rewards. He knew it had been true of his decision not to take a subscription to Dr. Excel's newsletter.

"I think I understand," said Evan, hopefully.

Dr. Excel knew that it takes a lot to change the average dentist, but he heard a sincerity in Evan's' voice and asked, "So, what can I do for you, Evan?"

"Well, it's been two years since I read your book. Initially, I had lots of enthusiasm for the changes you outlined. I made many of them and it had a dramatic impact on my practice. But now I'm stalled. I'm much better off today than I was before but I feel I could be doing better. Also, my enthusiasm and that of my team is gone. I was wondering if you had some secret that was not covered in the book that might wake us up?" asked Evan.

"Let's deal with you first," said Will.

"Okay," said Evan.

Dr. Excel looked at his watch.

"I don't have time to go over this now," said Will. "Call me at home tonight."

"That would be really great," said Evan, in disbelief.

Will gave Evan his home phone number and then went back to doing what he loves the most and does best --- making his patients happy.

Dr. Plateau immediately called back Dr. Excel's staff and ordered the newsletter.

Chapter Two

Continuing Education...Part Of The Job
The More I Learn, The Less I Know

"Hello."

"Hi, Will. This is Evan. Is this a good time?"

"Sure, Evan. Where were we?" asked Will.

"You were going to tell me how to get back my enthusiasm," said Evan.

"How do you feel about your dentistry?" asked Will.

"I don't know what you mean," said Will.

"Are you cocky about your skills?" asked Will. "What do you think of your work?"

"I guess it's OK," said Evan, tentatively, "But I don't know. It could be better, I guess. I sometimes wonder how it compares to others."

"Do you sometimes feel guilty about your fees?" asked Will.

"Yeah. I guess so. Why?" asked Evan.

"My friend, dentistry is really a tough business," said Will, passionately. "*Really tough!* Your day is dictated to you. People are depending on you. Many times you have to work without a break, even if you don't feel like it.

"Dentistry is very demanding. It requires both acute visual and manual dexterity while working in a tight environment.

"The point is, do not undervalue your importance and what you deserve. You are providing a very valuable service to humanity. Everyone who receives your service is better off because of it.

"What about sports? What value to humanity does Shaquille O'Neal provide? He makes multi-millions for having fun. Do people hate him for his success? Absolutely not! They love him. Why should you feel guilty about the amount of money you make?"

"I just...," stammered Evan. "I guess I just don't want my patients to object to me, well, getting rich off them. I bet they resent it."

"Listen," declared Will. "Your patients want you to be successful. If you needed brain surgery, would you want the unsuccessful surgeon in town operating on you?"

"No, of course not," said Evan.

"Sure, they may make a remark or two, but who cares?" said Will. "People like to complain, but they will continue to come to you, in fact, are more *likely* to continue to come to you *because* you're successful. People don't want to think they're stupid, and going to an unsuccessful doctor *is* stupid! Deep down, people know they get what they pay for, and they know that the unsuccessful doctor is not very good."

"I see what you mean," said Evan.

"Convince your patients that you are worth that amount, and then you are," declared Will. "And remember, a fair fee is anything the patient is willing to pay and you are willing to accept without remorse.

"And what about this self-esteem issue?" continued Will. "According to Walter Hailey and his Planned Marketing Research Inc., 90% of the dentists have a lower than average level of self esteem. And we feel guilty about making a decent living. Apparently, 30% of the dentists do 70% of the business of dentistry. It's that 30% that don't buy the bull and realize that they are far better dentists when they are adequately compensated.

"For example, Evan, if you won 6 million dollars in the state lottery, you would be a much better dentist, do you know why?" asked Will.

"Um, well..."

"Because, you'd be doing it for the fun, not the money," said Will. "You would only do the things you enjoy doing, and wouldn't worry about how much it's costing you. You would charge enough so you could take the time and do it right. You wouldn't care if the patients didn't come to you because you wouldn't need the money. The irony is that you would make more money than you do now!

"There is a story about a very successful tree trimmer. When asked about his success, he explained that before he went out on a bid, he always put five $100 bills in his pocket. This made him feel he didn't need the money. He never took a job for less than he felt it was worth and in doing so, he did a better job because he was adequately paid, which in turn created happy clients who gave him referrals. All because he presented an attitude of success at the first meeting with his clients.

"Recently I tried to slow down. I was getting too busy. So, I raised my fees by an average of 20% on most procedures. Guess what? My business increased! Why? Because I use service as a marketing edge. The point is, it's your fear that prevents you from success, not your patients. So stop worrying about what your patients will think and most importantly, stop listening to well-intentioned but misleading comments about how it's a crime to be profitable in health care, *BECAUSE IT'S NOT!"*

"You know, Will," said Evan, "I already feel better. You are dead right. I never thought about it. But what if I still wonder about my abilities. I mean, I think I'm a good dentist, but how do I know?"

"Let me ask you this," said Will. " If you thought your patients couldn't get better service anywhere else in town, would you feel bad about your fees?"

"Maybe that's why I wonder about my fees -- because I think I <u>could</u> do better," confessed Evan.

"Do you remember when you first learned the techniques you are currently performing?" asked Will.

"Yeah. I was all excited and couldn't wait to implement them in my practice," replied Evan, enthusiastically.

"Wouldn't it be great to feel like that about dentistry again -- to get back that feeling," asked Will.

"Yes, but how?" asked Evan.

"Have you read "The Pursuit of WOW!' by Tom Peters?" asked Will.

"No."

"Read it. In it you will find out how long it takes to become an excellent dentist." Will said. "Do you know the answer?"

"I, I don't know," stammered Evan.

"A nanosecond!" exclaimed Will.

Evan was doubtful, but continued to listen.

"Thomas Watson, the founder of IBM, said *If you want to achieve excellence, you can get there today. As of this second, quit doing less than excellent work.'*

"A drug addict or alcoholic can become drug-free in a nanosecond," continued Will, "but he spends the rest of his life maintaining that commitment. The same is true for excellence in dentistry. At first it may be difficult. You'll do things wrong, but that won't mean you're not an excellent dentist. We all make mistakes, but the excellent dentist learns from his or her mistakes.

"You need to take courses, read books and journals, listen to audio tapes, watch video tapes and visit other excellent dental offices. And you need to do all these on a continuing basis until the day you hang up the drill!

Evan was still quiet.

"But, it only takes a nanosecond to become an excellent dentist. It starts with your first patient tomorrow. Picture yourself as the world's greatest dentist and then start acting accordingly. The first step is to get the determination to do it. The rest is maintaining that commitment. For that you need to do three things: Keep your spirits up through the trials and tribulations, learn something new everyday, and do the right thing, the right way, until it becomes second nature to you.

"How many continuing education courses do you take a year?" asked Will.

"Maybe five," answered Evan, somewhat embarrassed.

"One of the biggest problems in our profession is that the majority of dentists don't take *any* continuing education courses," stated Will. "And if they do, they sign in and leave long before it's over. They only take these because their state has a minimal requirement, which is a joke in itself. A lot of states require only 12 units and those can be obtained by attending dental society meetings. The problem is that dentists don't know what they don't know. In fact, they are unaware that they don't know it. Dentistry is so complex and changing so fast, that you could study dentistry every day for the rest of your life and still not know everything. In fact, the more I learn, the less I realize I know!

"Five courses. Our profession thinks that's a lot, but I think it's terrible. I think you should make going to courses part of your job. Think of it as going to work. In fact, you should set aside two days a month to go to a program. The best dentists I know go to more than 200 hours a year. You need well over 100 hours a year to keep up with the changes taking place in dentistry.

"Contentment breeds mediocrity and you should never be content with what you know or what you're doing," said Will. "Find out what you don't know. It will rejuvenate your enthusiasm as you learn and comprehend. If you're interested in a particular aspect of dentistry, research it and take advanced training in that direction. Find others who feel like you do and network with them. Become so good at that aspect of dentistry that you are convinced that you can provide your patients the best treatment they can receive in your area. Become the local expert. When that happens, you will feel so good about your skills that you can't help but feel excited about what you do for a living."

"Yes," said Evan, excitedly, "I would feel good if I felt that I was an expert in a particular area."

"But it has to be in an area of dentistry that you enjoy and are interested in," warned Will. "It's hard to be good at something you don't enjoy doing."

"Okay, you're right," agreed Evan.

"Have you ever **not** gone to a course that you really wanted to go to because of its cost?" asked Will.

"I have," admitted Evan, somewhat embarrassed.

"And have you ever gone to a course that was lousy?" asked Will.

"Yes, plenty," said Evan. "And I think that's why I am reluctant to spend too much for a program."

"Did you ever go to a program that had a dramatic impact on your practice?" continued Will.

"Sure," said Evan.

"With the lousy ones, did you learn absolutely nothing -- not one bit of useful information?" asked Will.

"No, I can't say that I didn't always pick up at least one thing," replied Evan.

"My point is that while you may hit a few losers, even in those you picked up one or two worthwhile things. Therefore, if you had stopped going to seminars because of the losers, you would not have experienced those that had dramatic impact on your practice and your life," said Will.

"Yeah, I guess you're right," agreed Evan.

"It goes back to what I told you earlier," said Will. "You have to spend money to make money. The smart businessperson continues the search for the investment that will make a dramatic difference in his or her profits. *Education is just another business investment.*"

"I never looked at it like that," admitted Evan. "If I believed I was being paid to attend, I wouldn't hesitate."

"Now you're getting it!" exclaimed Will. "It's part of your job, and just as some aspects of your job are less profitable than others, the same can be said of courses you attend.

"I see," said Evan.

"I bet you've probably lost money on a few patients," said Will.

"Boy, that's the truth," said Evan.

"Did it stop you from going to work the next day, Evan?" asked Will.

"No, of course not," said Evan.

"Education should be viewed by us as an adjunct to income" stated Will. "What's more, every time you attend a good program you get a shot of enthusiasm. It's a challenge and it's exciting."

"You are right, Will," said Evan. "I will take my calendar and insert two seminar dates each month and make a conscious effort to find programs in the area I want to excel, which, by the way, is cosmetic dentistry. Then, I'm going to sign up for those programs."

"That's great, Evan," said Will, "but you need to do other things as well."

"Like what?"

"First, find a dentist you want to emulate," said Will. "If he's local, find out what he did and what courses he took to get where he is today. If he's nationally prominent, take his programs or his suggestions on what to attend. Most of the excellent clinicians are more than willing to help."

"Anything else?"

"Start enjoying what you are doing," said Will. "If you don't like an aspect of dentistry, stop doing it. And conversely, since you are interested in cosmetics, diagnose more of it."

"How do I do that?" asked Evan. "I don't want to be pushy or have my patients think I am trying to get money out of them. Could you teach me to communicate the need for esthetics to my patients?"

"I'd be happy to, but right now I've got to have dinner with my family," said Will, happily. "Call me tomorrow evening and we'll talk about your office team and how to get them excited about doing what you want them to do. Okay?"

"That would be great!" exclaimed Will. "Thanks for taking time to do this. You don't know how much I appreciate it."

"No problem, Evan," said Will. "Glad to help."

When Evan hung up he felt some of the excitement he had when he first read about Dr. Excel. He felt the powerful stimulant that knowledge and learning can be and felt somewhat angry with himself for nearly halting that process.

Evan thought about what Will had said about Omer Reed -- about how you don't know what you don't know and about the thrill of the journey to knowledge. He made a promise to himself: He would never stop, or slow down, the journey again.

Chapter Three

Creating The Super Employee
Low Base Pay, High Incentive Pay

The next day Evan talked to his staff about his goals. To his great disappointment he was met with a lack of enthusiasm and their part. When he left the staff meeting he knew that they hoped this reborn enthusiasm would simply go away - as it had before.

He realized that they didn't want to change anything. They were comfortable. He also knew they all wanted more money and yet he felt they didn't fully appreciate the things he already gave them. As a group they were unmotivated.

He also knew that it had not always been that way.

He was confused and somewhat hurt by the reaction of his staff. He hoped that Dr. Excel could answer his questions, but when he went to dial the phone he also felt a pang of guilt for taking up the doctor's evening again. He realized that he was finding it difficult to ask for the help he needed.

Evan took a deep breath and dialed the phone.

Evan almost hung up when Mrs. Excel answered the phone.

"Is Will home?" he asked.

"May I tell him who's calling?" Mrs. Excel asked, graciously.

Evan wondered if Mrs. Excel minded that her husband gave up his evening hours this way and wondered how it affected their personal life. He assumed he was not the only dentist who called him with these kinds of questions. He felt uncomfortable, but decided that it was less of a disruption to Dr. Excel at home than while he was working and felt a sense of appreciation overcome him as he waited.

"Hi, Evan, how's it going?" said Will.

"Just fine, Will. Sorry to bother you."

"No problem, just doing a few chores. This gives me an excuse to stop," chuckled Will.

"Tell your wife I'm sorry for taking your time," said Evan.

"Sure thing. Now where were we?" asked Will.

"Well, as excited as I am -- and I am really charged up -- I struck out today talking to my staff," explained Evan. "I really need some pointers. How do I get my team excited again?"

"Let's talk about compensation first," said Will. "You are using the 'piece of the pie payroll' that you learned about in the "The Exceptional Dental Practice," aren't you?"

"Yes, and it works great," said Evan. "They understand the concept of running a business because of it and never ask me for a raise, but the enthusiasm that they once had is gone. Although I have one team member who is terrific! She does most of the big cases and carries more than her share of the burden. How can I reward her and motivate the others to be more like her?"

"In "Thriving on Chaos," by Tom Peters, it says that a salary is nothing more than a reward for just showing up. You need a low base pay and high incentive pay. Tie your performance to what you want them to do. Reward that performance and it will be repeated. Ignore a performance, and it will usually cease. The best way to eliminate a good behavior is by not recognizing it.

"Rewards must be tied to measurable performances, or it appears you play favorites," said Will. "If it can be measured or charted, they can see for themselves who is deserving. There will be no arguments or hard feelings."

"Can you be more specific?" asked Evan.

"Okay," said Will. "What do you want your team to do more of?"

"I would like them to sell more veneer cases," said Evan.

"Then reward them for doing that," said Will. "Give them X number of dollars for each case sold that didn't come into your office for that purpose or that you didn't sell. Don't ignore your hygienist. They can be your best salesperson. She has that hour to sit there and convince them of the value of what you can do. Make it a substantial reward so they will work hard to do it."

"What is a substantial amount?" asked Evan.

"Share the wealth a little, and everyone wins," said Will. "I give my team $100 a case. If two of them helped sell the case, I divide it. Is it worth it for me to give them that for a $6,000 to $8,000 case? I think so, don't you?"

"You bet!" exclaimed Evan.

"Do the same for anything else that you want to happen," said Will. "Tomorrow I will fax you a sheet with a list of our office's rewards. Use it as a guide. Is there anything else you want them to do? Maybe a small thing, that they are neglecting?"

"Yes," said Evan. "I want them to fill out their checklists for each patient."

"Then give them a reward for not missing a day of the month," said Will. "I used to want them to collect payment without accepting insurance assignments. I would reward each treatment coordinator for keeping their accounts receivable below $5,000 a month, and twice that reward if it was below $2,500 a month. I had one treatment coordinator who was always below the $2,500 level, but the other was using insurance as a crutch so she wouldn't have to get forceful. So last year we stopped accepting insurance as co-payment. By taking away her crutch, her accounts receivable dropped dramatically."

"I would love to eliminate insurance from my practice," said Evan.

I'll tell you how, but first let me tell you about my treatment coordinators and their friendly competition. Whoever collects the most in the month, get an extra $50. It is a trackable item since each patient is assigned a treatment coordinator in the computer. We run a collection report for the providers at the end of the month and the winner gets the extra reward.

"The little things encourage your team to perform in the manner you want. I am not a believer in rewarding for seniority. It's just a reward for showing up for a long time and doesn't mean that person is doing a better job than the less senior members of the team. These other type of incentives, however, keep everyone on their toes and producing the desired results."

"That makes sense," said Evan. "But do the senior members resent it when a less senior employee gets more that month than they do?"

"They can't, since the rewards are measurable," said Will. "The other team member did a better job for the practice than they did. Granted, it works best in a frontdeskless office, where all aspects of care are handled by the one treatment coordinator. But even in a conventional office setup, there is no arguing with statistics."

"Yes," said Evan, enthusiastically, but I bet that's not all."

"You're right," said Will. "You need to hire people persons. The mistake most dentists make is that they hire dental skills and ignore the people skills. Dental skills can be taught. People skills are harder -- if not impossible -- to teach.

"Also, fire any employee who is a price-buyer, or at least try and fix them. You can't stress quality consciousness to your patients if your team member is price-conscious. They need to understand the value of quality to make the patients understand it."

"That makes a lot of sense," said Evan.

"The real problem is that the dentist is usually the most price-conscious person in the office," said Will. "They have no business training, they work hard for their money, and the result is that they are price-conscious. It's too bad. If they learned to appreciate quality more, they would feel better about their fees. When the dentist and the team feel good about their fees, the patients are more apt to feel the dentistry is worth the investment."

Evan quietly absorbed this knowing it was very true. Then he had an idea.

"Will, would you be willing to come to our study club and answer questions about the frontdeskless philosophy?" he asked.

"Sure," agreed Will.

"We meet on Tuesday. Would next week at 7:00 P.M. be okay?" asked Evan.

"See you then," said Will as he wrote the appointment in his daily planner. "In the meanwhile, work on your incentives and have a great weekend."

"I will, and thanks so much," said Evan. "I really appreciate it."

Evan immediately called his study club colleagues to tell them about the good news.

The next day, as promised, the incentive guidelines came through the fax machine. It read as follows:

Bonus Incentives

☑ Case acceptance level (Tx Coordinators)
☑ Therapy acceptance level (Hygienists)
☑ All check lists completed
☑ Bleach cases sold
☑ Veneer cases sold (not including initial exam or those coming in for cosmetic consultation)
☑ Less than (x) openings or of hygiene per month (Hygiene Coordinators)
☑ All financial contract arrangements made (Tx Coordinators)
☑ Most collected (Tx Coordinators friendly competition)
☑ Positive comments on evaluation sheet from patients
☑ Negative comments on evaluation sheet (amount subtracted)
☑ Referrals
☑ Tx room stocked with adequate supplies the entire month
☑ Carnation given to every female patient
☑ Hot towel given to every patient
☑ Evaluation form given to every patient
☑ Bun warmers sent

Chapter Four

Frontdesklessness Misunderstood
It's Just Patient-Centered Treatment

"Good evening, doctors," said Will as he entered Dr. Skeptic's waiting room.

It was a modest office with conventional dental decorations. The furniture was old and soiled. The magazines were aged and mostly lacked covers. The couches were low and sunken, and more fitting for a home setting.

Dr. Excel observed the decor and thought how difficult it must be for the senior citizen patients to get out of such couches. The colors were those used in the 1970's dental office. There were eight men and one woman sitting in the room, some who looked content and a few who looked as though they hoped this meeting would be short.

"Hi, Will," said Evan as he offered his hand. "I'm Evan. It's good to finally meet you. Let me introduce you."

"I'd love to meet everyone," said Will.

"This is John Skeptic," said Evan. "It's his office. We hold our meetings here because he has the largest waiting room."

Dr. Skeptic nodded without smiling, all the while keeping his nose ever so slightly in the air. Will disarmed him with a broad smile and a friendly wave.

"This is Fonda Kidds," said Evan. "She's the only pedodontist in our group."

Evan continued around the room, pointing to each person as he gave their name. "I.B. Frugle, founder of our group. Bill M. Phast, Bob N. Annout, Ty Little, William Triet, and Nevel Wurk."

"Hi everyone," said Will. "Nice to meet you."

William Triet came up, pumped Will's hand and said, "I'm so glad you're here. I've wanted to ask you questions for a long time."

A few of the others nodded their heads in agreement.

"Let's get started," Will said as he looked around for a place to sit.

"Right here," Fonda said, as she pointed to an over-sized chair at the head of the arrangement.

"Thank you Fonda," said Will. "Go ahead, everyone and ask me anything you want -- short of personal questions, that is." The other doctors chuckled and visibly relaxed as a result of Dr. Excel's demeanor.

"I guess the first question is, why the frontdeskless office?" asked Evan. "Most of us have read "The Exceptional Dental Practice," but what's the real advantage?"

Evan actually had been frontdeskless since reading the book. In fact, he was the sole member of the group to adopt the philosophy.

"Why <u>not</u> frontdeskless?" countered Will.

"Well, if things are going okay, why rock the boat?" asked Dr. Skeptic in a cocky tone. "I mean, I'm doing the ADA average, have been for years. I don't think I want to risk losing what I have."

"The idea is a more patient-centered practice," said Will. "We are entering the 21st century, and there is going to be a large chasm between the average guy and the top 10% of the practices. The difference will be the service. The frontdeskless environment will offer the patients better service and will create missionaries for your practice. **<u>Fortune</u>** magazine just reported that Marriot Hotels are going frontdeskless, although they call the individual a GSA, or 'guest service associate.' We call them Treatment Coordinators. At Marriot the person is everything to the guest, from bellman, check-in clerk, concierge - you name it, he or she does it. What was the point of this change? Customer service! The customer is placed in a friendly, warm environment where the GSA handles all the details of their stay. Guess what? The guest leaves thinking he has a friend at the hotel."

"Same thing can apply to dental offices. Conventionally, 75% of the communication in the office is among the team members. The front telling the back what needs to be done, and the back telling the front what occurred as they hand off the patient to one another."

"When a patient calls with a particular question, the front desk has to ask those in the back what transpired that day. When entering data in the computer the front desk may misread something, or get distracted due to interruptions. With a treatment coordinator, there are no distractions as his or her sole role is to cater to the patient in the operatory. He or she was present when the treatment was done, so entering data is easy. It all boils down to this: The more communication required among the team members, the more room for miscommunication.

"I work out of 4 operatories," said Dr. Bob N. Annout, jumping into the conversation. "Can it work for someone who is as busy as I am?"

"First, I want to talk about you working out of four operatories," said Will, shaking his head. "You could produce more money if you worked smarter, not harder. Also, you would feel better about the quality of work you performed. What type of restorations do you mostly place during the day?"

"Amalgam's, of course," replied Dr. Annout. "Don't you?"

"I haven't placed an amalgam in eight years," replied Will. "Would you put one in your mouth?"

"No, but that's what insurance will pay for," said Dr. Annout.

"So, you let insurance dictate your treatment, without even consulting with the patient on their choice," said Will, angrily. "I think that borders on malpractice. Why not teach them what you know then let them make their own decision? Empower them with knowledge and they will surprise you with their options.

"I work on one patient at a time, and I don't leave that patient until I am done. At that point I move to the other treatment coordinator's operatory and work on that patient. I don't room-hop. I take my time. Occasionally I finish with time to spare so I can sit and socialize with the patient. The difference is that I do only quality restorations and won't seat anything if I wouldn't seat it in my own mouth.

When you do this and forget about how much it will cost you to redo it, the financial rewards come rolling in because you are giving this patient a service they won't get elsewhere, and if quality is perceived, they will pay extra for it!

"Besides, Bob, you're going to kill yourself if you keep up this pace. At least you will get burned out on dentistry and quit before you're ready."

"I am already burned out," said Bob quietly.

"Me, too!" cried Bill M. Phast.

"So was I before I made this philosophical change," said Will. "But now I love dentistry again and I want you and every dentist to love what you do. It would be a better profession if every dentist loved his job. Incomes would go up and the best and brightest would be going into our profession.

"When I started school, 21,000 students took the Dental Aptitude Test. Last year only 7,000 took it. No one wants to be a dentist because of the return on their investment and because of how hard we work. If you slowed down and provided quality service, everyone wins. Your patient wins because they get better dentistry, you win because you aren't killing yourself and you're making more money, and the team wins because they aren't running on pure chaos. Of course, you need education to hone your skills. I have already talked to Dr. Plateau about that and he can fill you in."

"How can you slow down without losing money, and who is going to answer the *phone*?" asked Dr. Nevel Wurk.

"We'll talk about fees in a bit, I promise," said Will, "but I doubt you can have more phone calls than I have. I really have two full time jobs -- my seminar job, which brings in numerous phone calls from laboratories, societies, associations and doctors all around the world. Then, I run a full-time practice, which encounters the usual number of calls.

"There is no one rule about phone management. We have a day tape that we put in when we get there in the morning. It says 'We are all busy providing exceptional dentistry for our patients, so please leave your name and number and we will call you back as soon as we are available.' We also have a lunch tape, weekend tape, evening tape and special seminar tape when I am gone lecturing. I know other doctors who are frontdeskless who use voice mail or an answering service. On the other end, one really busy practice I know hired an unskilled people person to do nothing but answer the phones.

"All patient communication and care is still handled in the operatory so there is no need to bring the patient up front to be checked out. The frontdeskless philosophy reduces the phone calls from patients since communication in the office is improved. We also give patients written instructions to eliminate the extra phone calls."

"I don't have computers in my operatories," said Dr. I.B. Frugle. "Can I do everything in the operatories without them?"

"Computers in the operatories make life easier, but aren't absolutely essential," said Will. "In fact, we didn't use a computer for scheduling for years. We had a book for treatment, and one for hygiene. All other entries, however, were made on the operatory terminals.

"But don't nickel and dime your practice, I.B. Think of it as an investment. Consider what the monthly payment will be, instead of the big ticket price. Get the piece of equipment if it will make life easier, more efficient and give you a return on your investment.

"However, to properly care for your patients and market your practice, you desperately need a computer. That doesn't mean you have to have one to be frontdeskless. It just helps. I know a doctor who has a computer only in the front office area. He maintains the frontdeskless philosophy with treatment coordinators who bring their patient up front to enter the treatment, schedule their next visit and collect the money. It works, but it takes the patient out of the private environment of the operatory. He is successful doing that, so I have no qualms about it.

"Another doctor has one case presenter. The treatment coordinators do everything else. I don't particularly like this as it takes the most important connection with the patient and gives it over to someone else. My fear is that they will think of the case presenter as their office liaison instead of the treatment coordinator. But this doctor is happy and apparently it works for him. The philosophy is still intact with the game board slightly altered."

"I don't know, it seems so weird," said Dr. Ty Little.

"Gees, Ty," barked Dr. Triet, "You'll never change. You still think fiberoptic hand pieces are just a passing fad!"

Everyone laughed as Dr. Little turned beet red.

"If it's so good, why aren't the physicians operating this way?" asked Dr. Little.

"Physicians see a patient every five minutes," said Will. "They need a traffic cop. We have always emulated physicians, but it doesn't apply in a high quality dental office. I see one patient every 40 minutes to 60 minutes, on average. With that spacing, a traffic cop up front is totally unnecessary."

"I'm still worried about insurance," said Bill M. Phast, shaking his head. "Who handles the barrage of forms that come in and out of the office? We must be on top of it to get paid as soon as possible. Unfortunately, we often have outstanding bills from insurance companies going for months. It's the biggest pain in the butt in our office!"

"Let me interrupt before you answer that question, Will," said Evan. "It might be a good time to talk to about becoming insurance independent."

"Let's do it," said Will, enthusiastically. It was one of his favorite subjects.

Chapter Five

Becoming A Non-Insurance-Dependent Dentist
Slaying the Insurance Dragon

"**W**hat determines the fees for most all your procedures?" asked Will.

"Insurance, I guess," said Dr. Phast.

The others nodded in agreement.

"Isn't that brilliant?" said Will, sarcastically.

Everyone laughed as Will continued.

"Do you realize that they are your enemy? In order for them to do good, you have to do bad. They make money when you don't. If they paid you a lot, they would lose a lot. It has to be a win/lose situation. They are in effect, your enemy. Why would you let your enemy determine your fees?

"What is the average maximum annual benefit for an insurance company today?" asked Will.

"Usually $1,000," replied Fonda.

"Do any of you know what the maximum annual benefit in the 1960's was?" asked Will.

A silence fell across the group. He knew no one had the answer. He paused to allow his next statement more weight.

"One thousand dollars!" exclaimed Will.

"Gees!" said Bob. The others in the group shook their heads in disgust.

"If you add in the cost of living since 1970, the maximum benefit today should be $3,700," said Will. "When insurance begged to get involved in dentistry back in the 60's, $1,000 was a lot of money. Most were excited because it would mean that more people would have their work done. The problem is that once they got in, they took over control of our profession.

"Perhaps like Bob, you don't do certain restorations because insurance doesn't pay for it. Even though you believe it to be the best restoration, maybe you don't even *offer* it to your patients. I believe this borders on malpractice. No doctor has the right to do *anything* but the very best for his or her patient.

"The fact that 85% of Americans have periodontal disease is our fault. We allowed insurance to dictate treatment. Most insurance companies will only pay for two cleanings a year, so that is what we schedule, even though 85% of Americans need more than that. If we would educate the public they would have more cleanings, regardless of what insurance will pay. But dentistry has let the insurance industry take over the diagnosis, treatment and control of our profession. When you let an insurance consultant decide how to treat your patients, you are telling your patients that the consultant knows more about dentistry than you do when the truth is they are generally the worst dentists in their area.

"What can we do about this problem?" asked Bill.

"Take control of your own practice," said Will. "Don't sign up for any PPO's, HMO's or closed panels. Most PPO's promise you tons of patients. One recent ad for a PPO in a trade journal bragged about the fact that you would only have to reduce your fees by 20% to receive all these patients. Sound good Bill?"

"It might be, if enough patients came in," said Dr. Phast.

"What is the profit margin in your office?" asked Will.

"About 25%," said Bill.

"Have you ever seen the Kodak study?" asked Will.

"What's that?" asked Bill.

"Basically, it says that with your profit margin, if you reduced your fees 20%, you would have to increase your business by 400% to make the same amount of money," said Will, with a scowl. "Would you like to work four times as hard and make the same amount of money?"

"No way," said Bill. "I already work too hard!"

"Most guys -- and I apologize, Fonda, I use the term generically, like 'his' for his or hers -- especially young dentists, can't see the trap," said Will. "When you sign up for a PPO or other such program, you are treating *their* patients not yours. Those patients are going to you because *you* are on *their* list. You get *off* their list and they go somewhere else. There is absolutely no loyalty with those patients. If you want out, you're trapped because you would have to start your practice all over again. I know many dentists struggling with this and who hate dentistry because of it. According to last years ADA income survey, the dentists who practice in strictly preferred provider, HMO's or closed panel type of offices had the lowest average income.

"By signing up you are helping to destroy the profession. Everyone who signs up puts another nail in the coffin of dentistry's future. For your own sake, and for the profession's sake, don't do it. Where would these things be if no one participated? They wouldn't be in existence, that's where. They can't exist without dentists signing up for them. Don't fall for their scare tactics that say it's inevitable. It's NOT! If only a few dentists signed up for them they would fall apart, because mostly the worst dentists sign up and the patients won't tolerate that kind of care. You don't need them, but boy do they need you!

"You think that I am angry about this?" asked Will. "Well, I am! It's ruining one of the finest professions in the world. It makes dentists do substandard work or even dishonest things to make a decent living. These plans perpetuate inferior dentistry. A guy *has* to room hop in order to make a decent living. If he is in a HMO, it pays for him to *not* diagnose treatment because he gets paid the same whether he does work or not. Human nature is such that if you're paid the same regardless if you work or don't work, you won't work. I know I wouldn't! It also prevents you from bringing your patients in for continued care visits or cleanings. The problem is, the public doesn't understand this because it's never been explained to them."

"You convinced me," said Bill. ""I'm dropping my PPO tomorrow."

"Me too!" said Bob.

"But I don't think my patients will let me eliminate insurance," said Dr. Nevel Wurk.

"Yeah, how exactly can we become insurance independent?" asked Ty.

"You need to retrain your patients," said Will. "You've trained them to expect you to accept insurance as payment. When you or your staff presents their bill you usually say something like:

> *'Your portion will be $300 Mrs. Jones.'*

"You don't even ask them if they want the insurance to pay you. Before our office eliminated insurance as a method of payment, we never brought up insurance unless they did. If they asked if we accepted their insurance as partial payment, we told them we would work with their insurance *if* there is a financial burden. If, however, the insurance company takes longer than 30 days to pay, they were assessed a finance charge. Regardless, the balance was their responsibility, not that of the insurance companies.

"Most patients would say things like: 'Oh, it's not a financial problem, I'll and pay and have the insurance company pay me,' or, 'I don't want a finance charge, so I'll have them reimburse me.' You would be shocked at the response.

"First, eliminate insurance from your hygiene department immediately. Give the patient a walkout slip to send with their insurance forms. Most people can afford to pay to have their teeth cleaned. In fact, we have devalued this service by undercharging and not requiring people pay for it at the time of the visit."

"If they can't afford to have their teeth cleaned, tell them they can put it on their charge card. The insurance check company will come before they get their credit card bill. Eliminating hygiene insurance would eliminate approximately 300 insurance forms a month for you. Wouldn't that be nice?"

"Boy, it sure would!" exclaimed Dr. Triet, as the others shook their heads in agreement.

"But, how do we get the patient to have the dentistry that insurance won't pay for?" asked Nevel. "Since they will only pay for the cheapest material available -- the amalgam -- how can we get them to accept the quality stuff?"

"You need to convince them their out-of-pocket expense is worth it," said Will. "You do this through proper education. No one values what they don't understand. Videos are good, but explore a multi-media format. Come to my office and I'll show you mine."

"Great, I'd love that," said Nevel. The others agreed.

"We will set something up in the future," said Will.

"The next step is to eliminate insurance all together and to do this, you need to provide a service that an insurance-*dependent* dentist can't provide. I'll show you all that when you come to my office for the tour.

"Don't get me wrong," said Will. "We do everything in our power to get the insurance companies to reimburse the patient for the work performed. We will write nasty letters, send in pictures or any needed information, and even call and yell at the company, but we just don't *wait* for payment. It's easier for the patient to keep track of their *one* insurance form than for us to keep track of *hundreds*."

"It sure would be," said Evan.

"But you must explain the advantage to the patients. Tell them that you are doing this to improve your relationship with them. In essence you are, because insurance problems cause rifts. Tell them you are containing health care costs by eliminating the costs of managing an insurance-driven practice and that you would have to hire another employee to handle the insurance claims at a cost that would be passed on to them. There are many options that will work and they are all true."

"It is much nicer not to deal with the hassles of the insurance companies. The small accounts receivable I had before was due to the few patients that my one treatment coordinator allowed to use insurance. Eliminating it eliminated all the problems."

"You mean you don't finance patient treatment?" asked Fonda, in obvious disbelief.

"No, and let me tell you why!" said Will.

Chapter Six

The No Finance Rule
Never Lend Money to Family, Friends....
and Patients

"**T**he saying goes, 'Never lend money to family and friends," said Bill. "Why is that?"

"Because it ruins relationships," said Dr. Triet.

"That's right, and lending money to patients is what you do when you finance their treatment," said Will. "People don't like those to whom they owe money. Your patients will feel the tension and find reasons to fault your work so they don't have to pay you. It's human nature. I experienced it myself when I built my new office, went $20,000 over budget and owed the contractor. I went around the office with a fine-tooth comb, finding little things wrong so I wouldn't have to pay them. When I realized what I was doing, I paid them and our relationship improved.

"Conversely, if they pay in advance, they will want to think they are smart, and find reason to love your work. The relationship with our patients improved dramatically as did the satisfaction with our work, when we adopted the no-finance policy."

"Didn't you lose patients?" asked Dr. Phast.

"Some, but you can't be everyone's dentist," said Will. "As Walter Haley says, 'Some will, some won't, so what ... NEXT!' Don't let one patient dictate your treatment philosophy. The problem is, most of you give the squeaky wheel the grease.

"However, you must provide them with a service they can't get from someone who will finance them.

"How do you present payment to the patients?" asked Evan.

"We have three choices," said Will. "They can pay up front for a 5% investment reduction. You would be amazed how many patients take advantage of this. Or, it can be broken down by the number of visits -- if the case is $5,000 and will take 10 visits, it's $500 per visit. Lastly, if they can't afford either, we finance them through third party financing company. They pay us and the patient owes them the monthly payments. This is not the same as financing your patients yourself. They hate the financing company, not you. You have been separated from their payment. Those are the options available to our patients. It works wonderfully."

"What if patients prefer an inferior treatment?" asked Ty.

"In our office most of the time it's not an option," said Will. "If they go somewhere else, they were not meant for our office. I have a lot of people referring me patients even though they don't come here. Kind of strange, don't you think?"

"Sure is, why do they refer to you?" asked Evan.

"They say that they can't afford me, but I'm the best dentist in town and I won't sacrifice my principles for money. Pretty nice backhanded compliment," said Will.

"Aren't you afraid of losing these patients?" asked Evan.

"The truth is, 20% of your patients cause 80% of your problems," said Will. "You eliminate these people and life is easier. What do you care if the whiners and the complainers go somewhere else? You don't have to treat everyone that walks in the door. It's OK not to and in fact you can't physically treat everyone in your town.

Does it take courage to *fire* a patient? If they're not enjoyable to work on, *fire them*. You spend most of your life in the office, so you might as well enjoy it! I'm giving you permission, in fact, I get some weird pleasure out of telling patients they would be better off elsewhere and then giving them the name of another dentist."

The group laughed in unison, most realizing that they too would enjoy telling a few of their patients to hit the road.

"The problem is," said Will, "the more I don't want them, the more they want me! I have a hard time getting rid of some of them. It's really part of the attitude of success. If you act like you don't need their money, they are eager to give it to you."

The group laughed again.

"But how do you get to the point that you are sure you will have enough patients to do that?" asked Evan.

"Let's hit on the real problem here," said Will.

Chapter Seven

Diagnosing Necessary Treatment
The Key to a Successful Practice

"Do you guys know the difference between a top 10% practice and the average dental practice?" asked Will. "Let me give you a hint: It's a one word answer."

"Marketing?" asked Fonda.

"No."

"Education?" asked Evan.

"While that *is* extremely important, it is not the word I am looking for," said Will.

A silence fell over the group as they wondered what Will was thinking.

"It's **DIAGNOSIS,**" said Will, emphatically.

"The main difference between the top dentists and the average dentist is the diagnosis of necessary work. There is enough work out there for everyone to be extremely busy. The average dentist is just afraid to diagnose necessary treatment and struggles with guilt feelings when diagnosing. He or she often is worried that the patient will think he's being ripped off. It's worse if he's a new patient who is coming from a dental practice where nothing had been diagnosed for a while. Tell me none of you have felt those feelings."

Everyone nodded with agreement. Some of them appeared ashamed.

"I know I will watch conditions as long as I can to avoid any conflicts," said Dr. Annout. "If I wait until the patient is in pain, it makes it easier to convince him to accept treatment.

"It is hard to suggest treatment to a patient who has recently been to a dentist that never recommended anything," said Evan. "I think they wonder if I am trying to make money off them and so I diagnose it later when the trust has been established."

"I want to tell you a related story," said Will.

"A dentist recently referred a patient to me. I diagnosed some work that was necessary: Four indirect composite restorations and four direct occlusal composites were required to replace old leaking amalgams with two teeth having obvious decay radiographically.

"This shocked the patient. She had been going to the other dentist who had not diagnosed anything in 17 years! She called him to see if he agreed with my diagnosis. He didn't, saying I was a high-end dentist with a high-end practice. I wrote him and asked about his response and he replied that since she had only one gold onlay done in 27 years, he didn't think the work was necessary. This meant that these amalgam fillings that I deemed unacceptable were over 27 years old -- far above the average life span the ADA suggests. He had disagreed with my recommendations and made this diagnosis of not treating them even though he had not examined her (by her request) on her continued care visits since

1988. Further, he had not taken X-rays since 1984, according to records she brought with her."

"You're kidding!" exclaimed Evan. "What did you do?"

"Well, thank the dental gods for intra-oral cameras. Because of his recommendations, the patient had not scheduled her work. I told her that there was obvious decay radiographically on a couple and if I removed one of the others that were not obvious radiographically (they were clinically, to me, at least) and there was no decay underneath, then she would not have to pay for those. I told her that if she didn't want me to do them she should have someone else do them before a problem arose. She told me that based on his original recommendation, she would only go to me and because of this confidence in my diagnosis, she scheduled to have all of the restorations replaced at once.

"I was so sure of my diagnosis that she decided to go ahead with my treatment. Since I was so confident, I was willing to do it for free. What did she have to lose?"

"How did you convince her that they were decayed?" asked Dr. Wurk.

"During treatment, I used the intra-oral camera to show her the decay," said Will. "The one that was obvious on the radiograph was much worse clinically and was close to a pulpal exposure. The small radiographically evident caries (he had disagreed with me on this one) was also blatantly carious once we got in and I showed her with the camera. Another that I thought was going to be a direct occlusal, was fractured mesially with caries present interproximally. All restorations had some amount of caries under them. I showed her these. This is why I believe the camera is so valuable. I gained an extreme amount of trust from her and I doubt she will *ever* question my opinion again."

"I know I couldn't practice without my intra-oral camera," said Evan.

"What's the point of this story?" asked Will. He didn't wait for an answer.

"This fine dentist reminds me of the Gallo Wine commercials. *'We will treat no tooth before it's time.'* He believed he was doing this patient a favor by under-diagnosing. Was he? He thought that by trying to make these restorations last as long as possible, he was being a good dentist for her. Was he? Is that how you want *your* mouth treated? Would it have been better to do endodontic treatment on the one that was close to a pulpal exposure by waiting longer?"

"Of course not," said Dr. Skeptic. "But what if you were wrong and there was no decay under a couple of them? Wouldn't it then have been better to wait?"

"I would have replaced a restoration a few years before it's time. Would that have been so terrible? The patient would have received a better restoration, in my opinion, and certainly a more esthetic and tooth-supportive one. To me, it was a no-lose situation. Eventually she would needed them replaced anyway. So, where is the harm? But I wasn't wrong, and we prevented the patient from experiencing any future problems. That philosophy may be good for wines, but it's a dangerous and unnecessary risk for dentistry."

The room was quiet while the group nodded their heads. Will looked at them.

"Why are we as dentists so afraid of diagnosing treatment?" he asked. "The top-end dentists diagnose necessary treatment without feeling guilty. They diagnose as if they were treating their own mouth. The average dentist avoids diagnosing because he or she is afraid the patient will think they are being ripped off. Treat every mouth as if it were yours and you can never go wrong."

"I understand," said Dr. Triet. "I will not feel guilty about diagnosing treatment anymore. But I do feel guilty about diagnosing esthetic inlays when I could just crown the teeth and they might last longer. I struggle with the issue of longevity and have some guilt with it. I feel bad if my restorations don't last forever."

"I'm glad you brought that up," said Will. "I really want to address that issue."

Chapter Eight

Conservatism vs. Longevity
Does Esthetics Preclude Quality?

"**M**y friend, Dr. Dave Hornbrook, wrote a column for his newsletter that I feel addresses this issue," said Will to begin his explanation.

"He was involved in a discussion with a prominent prosthodontist who had a tendency to crown everything because they last longer. Dave believes as I do, that a conservative restoration that may not last as long as an aggressive crown preparation, is better. We both believe that we would rather risk having to replace a restoration in our own mouth in 15 years rather than unnecessarily destroy healthy tooth structure for retentive purposes. In 15 years there will probably be a conservative esthetic material that will last as long as a conventional crown. There are so many other benefits with a conservative restoration as well, such as being kind to the opposing surface and kind to the tissue since no invasion of the gingival integrity is necessary to esthetically hide margins. That is why I place these restorations, as it is my choice for my *own* mouth. In fact, I just had Dave place three indirect esthetic restorations when I could have had any type done."

"It's the choice for my mouth also," said Evan. "But because it's esthetic dentistry, most dentists think it's less quality."

"This brings me to a subject that is prevalent in the minds of some dentists," said Will. "I did a three-weekend program for a study club in New Mexico. Most of the members were also members of a gold study club. Overcoming the resistance that a few of these dentists had towards esthetics was difficult. In fact, one quit the study club because he couldn't handle it. Their gold mentor was almost in tears trying to talk them out of doing esthetic restorations, or so I was told. When one of the more progressive ones in attendance asked one of the other members if he was going to do these types of restorations, he said he didn't think so because he wanted a *quality practice.* This goes back to the days where esthetics was thought to be unethical."

"I hear that all the time," said Evan.

"The problem with that statement is that *one does not preclude the other,*" said Will. "You can have a quality practice as well as an esthetic one. In fact, if you are doing *good* esthetic work, it *has* to be a quality practice. The problem is that they mistake quality with longevity, and they are not necessarily related.

"Some 10 or 15 years ago, a survey was done to determine how much a tooth was worth," said Will. "They questioned dental personnel on how much they would have to be paid to have one of their healthy front teeth crowned. Fonda, how much would I have to pay you to crown your healthy front tooth?"

"You couldn't pay me enough!" said Fonda, emphatically.

"In the study the average price to destroy one of *their* teeth and then crown it was $100,000. Many answered as Fonda did, that there was not enough money in the world."

The group chuckled in unison.

"But doesn't anything that last longer mean better quality?" asked Dr. Annout.

"An analogy is a gourmet meal versus an all-you-can-eat buffet," replied Will. "But which one is a quality meal?"

"The gourmet meal, of course," replied Bob.

"But the buffet will last you longer, stay with you longer and you get more food," said Will. "It may even repeat on you all night long so you get more for your money."

Everyone laughed.

"But is it quality?" asked Will. "Or is the elegantly cooked gourmet dinner, even though done in small portions, more of a quality meal? I think it is, and I would think you would agree."

"I have seen many poorly done conventional restorations responsible for periodontal disease, so no matter how long the restoration would last, the quality was not there. Poor quality can be in any type of material. Certainly, a more aggressive, tooth sacrificing preparation is necessary with a conventional cast restoration. To me, excessive removal of tooth structure is not quality. **Conservatism is!"**

"Wow!" exclaimed Dr. Triet. "For the first time in my career, I understand. I can feel good about my esthetic restorations."

Most of the group shook their heads in agreement.

"A guilt obsession is a negative emotion with no really positive value," said Will. "Remove the guilt from your life and do the right thing. Do the thing that you would do if you were treating yourself. Whatever that is, feel comfortable with your decision. I am not telling you how to practice or what restorations to do, just do what you feel is best and the treatment of choice for your own mouth. No doctor has the right to do anything but what they believe to be the very best for his or her patients.

"And with that, let's call it an evening, my friends," said Will. He looked at his watch. "I want to get home to my boy before he goes to bed. Why don't you decide on a date to come in to my office and I'll show you how to create an image that will make your patients perceive the value. Remember, if value is perceived, they will pay extra for it. It's the key to incorporating all the changes that we talked about."

"Great, Will," said Evan. "We'll talk about it and come up with a day that's good for all of us as well as for you."

Everyone jumped up and shook Will's hand. They thanked him for the enlightening evening. Even Dr. John Skeptic seemed to take on a new persona. Dr. Frugle, who had been silent most of the evening, asked how he could get his newsletter.

All in all, it was a good night for everyone. With heads spinning from all the new information, they left Dr. Skeptic's office and drove home.

Chapter Nine

Image Is Everything
Maybe Not, But It's Close

Dr. Plateau pulled up in front of Dr. Excel's office and parked as close to the door as possible. It was Sunday morning and the lot was empty. Evan had driven with Dr. Kidds, and William Triet. Dr. Frugle, Dr. Annout and Dr. Little arrived together in another car. It was a beautiful, clean, crisp fall day which made Evan think it was doubly hard for Will to give them some of his free time.

They exited the cars and walked toward Will's office door. The outside of the building was unassuming, yet classy. As they opened the door and approached the waiting room, they all stopped and simply stared.

"This place is beautiful!" said Fonda as Will walked up to greet the group.

"Thanks," said Will, who in that instant realized he had taken it for granted lately. "It's a nice place to work. You only have one chance to create a first impression. It's hard to recover from a bad one. We want our first impression to be, well, impressive."

"Nice waiting room!" exclaimed Evan.

He was gazing at the vaulted ceiling, and then at the waterfall in the wall.

"It's a greeting room," said Will. "Since we don't make patients wait, it's our 'greeting' area. We want them to feel like they're in someone's living room, not in a dental office. That's why you don't see any dental pictures on the wall. It immediately creates an image of quality. They think quality as soon as they enter the building."

"They also probably think expensive!" said Dr. Frugle.

"I hope so!" said Will with a laugh. "If they're in the wrong place, they might as well know it before wasting my time. I am setting the stage and this is the first step to educate the patient about quality dentistry. You create an image of quality then teach them about the value of quality dentistry. It's all part of the experience in our office."

"What's this?" asked Dr. Little. He was pointing to a counter with a coffee pot on top and a refrigerator underneath.

"It's our refreshment center," said Will. "With juice and other refreshments in the fridge and apples in the bowl, we encourage our patients to help themselves. It is another attempt to use service as a marketing edge and provide them something they didn't expect so they will become missionaries for us. It's extremely easy to market using service because most dentists won't."

Will looked around and asked, "Where are the others?"

"Bill and Nevel couldn't make it," replied Evan.

"That's too bad," said Will. He instantly understood that they had chosen not to attend. It happened a lot. In fact, he was aware that 80% of the dentists who hear something new will do nothing different. Even those who were there today might make no changes in their lives.

The excuses were old news to him. He believed that most dentists protect their fragile self esteems by not trying anything that might fail. He understood that to many, the possible bitterness of failure is worse than the potential sweetness of success. He, however, believed that there was no reason to fail with these principles and continued on with the group at hand.

"You don't have a door to the operatories!" announced Bob N. Annout. "Why not?"

"You should also notice we don't have one of those stupid sliding windows that separate *us* from *them*," said Will. "In my opinion, both create the image that we are hiding things from the patients. They must wonder what that is, of course. Maybe they think we drop instruments on the floor and then use them again! Who knows? We give all new patients a complete tour of the office. The most important tour is of the sterilization area. I can't tell you how many patients express relief at what they see and say it calms their fears.

"I don't want to create any barriers between me and my patients. They are part of our office family -- in fact the most important part. This is to be their dental home. We want them to be comfortable.

"Image is important because patients don't know how good your margins are or if you use the best lab. They don't know if you buy the best supplies -- as opposed to the cheapest. They only know what image you portray. You want that image to be of a quality dentist. If they are greeted by old magazines and old furniture when they walk in, they can only conclude .... *old dentistry*!

"You all know those who are not particularly good dentists, but have great practices. Why? because they know how to deal with people and they have created a good image. Likewise, there are also those who are great clinical dentists but have lousy practices, purely because they created a bad image and are jerks."

Everyone laughed.

Evan said, "Yeah, Nevel's like that. He's a good dentist, but has a terrible chairside manner."

"Well, let's continue the tour," said Will.

"What's this?" asked Dr. Triet, as he passed what looked suspiciously like a front desk. "I thought you said you were frontdeskless?"

"That's a greeting station," said Will with a smile. "We don't have anyone here, but we need an area for our business equipment and files, so we placed it close to the greeting room. If someone is working up here they can greet the patients as they enter. Remember, frontdesklessness is just a philosophy, not a physical requirement."

"My team does paper work up here, and makes their calls, but we don't service patients here," said Will. "All that is done in the operatories with either their treatment coordinator or hygiene coordinator. It's much more patient-centered and personal -- as well as private."

The group approached a wall of glass bricks. Fonda walked ahead and peered into the room behind it.

"Wow!" she cried. "What's this?"

"It's our interview room, our imaging room, our case presentation and education room. More simply put, it's our VIP room," said Will. "It is the first room a new patient comes to after the greeting room. We interview them in this room and create an image with the high-tech equipment. We also display photographs of esthetic dentistry here. It's part of creating the image of quality."

"What's this?" asked Dr. Frugle.

He was pointing at a computer monitor.

Chapter Ten

Creating A Value
Through Education
Computer-Assisted Education Systems

The group settled themselves in chairs around he computer monitor.

"Patient education is the key to creating an environment for the acceptance of high-end dentistry," said Dr. Excel. "If most patients knew what we knew, they would all choose quality dentistry over the cheap stuff."

"Well, most of us anyway," said Evan casting a look at Dr. Frugle.

Dr. Frugle rolled his eyes and forced a smile.

"Harold Wirth, a renowned dentist once said, *'People have money for what they want whether they need it or not. It's our job to make them want what they need.'* The problem is not that they can't afford it, but that it's not a priority. Do you realize that last year in the United States, $37 billion was spent on dental treatment, while $300 billion was spent on gambling?"

"You're kidding!" said Fonda, who looked shocked.

"No, and $300 billion was spent on alcohol, $50 billion on tobacco, and $40 billion on dog food," said Will. "So don't tell me that people don't have money for dentistry. They just don't *want* it! They don't *want* it because they don't *value* the service enough.

"The problem is that most dentists have neither the time nor the will to educate patients. In fact, organized dentistry has failed to inform the public about the wonderful advances in dentistry. That is because most dentists don't know about the advances. I was talking to a flight attendant the other day who has never heard of porcelain veneers. This is, of course, not uncommon, but it is unfortunate. Probably most people think porcelain veneers have something to do with toilets."

Everyone laughed at this suggestion.

"She had heard of liposuction, but not veneers," said Will. "She also has a PFM on #8 that is too opaque and exhibits a dark gingival margin. Her dentist wrongly told there was nothing to be done about it. I told her to call the American Academy of Cosmetic Dentistry and ask for a referral to an accredited dentist in her area. This is a perfect example of how poorly we have educated the public about the positive things available in dentistry."

"So, how do you use this thing?" asked Dr. Frugle, pointing to the monitor again.

Will tapped the machine.

"It's called the **CAESY system,**" said Will. "Hours of education on a CD ROM. It is also available on a CDI disc, to display it on regular TV The patient or you can choose the category -- even sub categories within a category -- and the computer explains the procedures in informative, yet simple format. You can also use the gallery or photographs and graphics to demonstrate your message yourself.

"Let me show you one section. Since I very seldom do PFM's -- instead opting for the all porcelain crown -- there is a sub-category I use a lot. Under the cosmetic section and the sub-category of crowns, is the subject of how the all-porcelain crown eliminates the dark line at the gum line and why that line occurs. In just a few minutes, with the use of pictures and graphics, your patient will understand the reason you want to do an all-porcelain crown and the need for the extra expense."

Dr. Excel began the program and sat back and watched the monitor with the others.

As the program ended he said, "This example is indicative of the remainder of the program. We've just seen a tip of the iceberg here. It is a vast amount of education material. I love the verbal explanations in the laymen's language. It can be used in the operatory, waiting room, or case presentation room, on a regular TV or a computer monitor. I love it!"

"How much does it cost?" asked Dr. Frugle, which caused the others to burst into laughter.

"Even *you* can afford it," said Will, with a smile. "In fact, you can't afford <u>not</u> to have it. I'll give you their number later, but I want you to read something I received from Dr. Ron Jackson, a friend of mine who lectures on esthetic dentistry. It explains what I am talking about. I'll give each of you a copy. Read it with me."

KNOW YOUR POTATOES

Two farm wagons stood in a public market, both loaded with potatoes. A housewife stopped beside the first wagon and asked, "how much are your potatoes today?"

"Dollar and a quarter," replied the farmer.

"I only paid a dollar last time," the woman protested.

"Taters have gone up," grunted the farmer and turned aside.

"At the next wagon, the housewife asked the same question, but Ma McGuire knew her potatoes.

"These are especially fine white potatoes," she said. "We raise only the kind with small eyes so there will be no waste in peeling. Then we sort 'em by sizes. In each bag you'll find a large size for boiling and cutting up, and a smaller size for baking. The baking size cooks quickly and uniformly."

"These potatoes are clean, too." she continued. "You could put a bag in the parlor without soiling your carpet -- you don't pay for a lot of dirt. They're a good buy at $1.65. Shall I have them put in your car?"

The woman who thought that the first farmer's potatoes were too high bought two bags from Ma McGuire at a higher price.

All of which proves that it is much more important to establish a value than to quote a price.

"This is what I am talking about," said Will after they had read through the story. "Educate your patients to the value and they will eagerly pay more for it. I promise."

Chapter Eleven

Using Service As A Marketing Edge
Five Star Service

Will walked into one of the operatories and pointed to the TV mounted on the wall.

"Since you all have read the "The Exceptional Dental Practice," you know how I feel about intra-oral video cameras. You have to have one if you're going to do the high-end dentistry. We give every patient a tour of the mouth during their exam. Most are amazed what they see. In fact, one woman brought her husband in and said, *'show him the camera. I told him there was no arguing with you with that thing, since you can see what you're talking about.'*

"Another man came in with *his* wife, and asked me if I knew his dentist. I told him I do. In fact, the dentist was helpful to me when I first got out of school. He then said jokingly, *'I want you to call him and tell him what a dump his office is!'* Apparently, it had been fine for this patient -- until he saw something better. You can be certain that your patients will see offices like this. You don't want them talking about your office that way, now do you?"

"No!" said most of the group, in unison.

"It's part of the image, and it's very important," said Will. "Let me show you a few things we do to create that image."

Will walked out of the operatory and faced a system of cabinets that contained two printers, credit card machines as well as glass cabinets with tray set-ups behind the glass. There was also a metal compartment with a handle on the front.

"Do you know what this is?" asked Will.

"No," responded the group.

"It's a warm towel dispenser," said Will as he pulled out a plastic packet and held it to his nose.

"It's lemon-scented," he said, as he handed a towel to Evan.

"What does it remind you of?" asked Will.

"First class on an airplane," said Evan.

"First class, you bet," said Will. "That is the image you want to portray! It's part of the five-star service we offer. Just like the personal service the frontdeskless environment provides. The carnations you saw at the greeting station, which we give to our female patients as they leave. The fresh flowers delivered weekly that we display on the coffee table in the greeting room. The refreshment center. The TVs they watch while having work done. Just like the phone calls to our patients at the end of the day to make sure they are okay. And let me show you another service that we do for our *cosmetic smile lift* patients."

Will led them to a large conference room decorated with photographic lights on either side of a hanging roll of black felt paper. He pulled down the paper, revealing the backdrop for photographs.

"We take studio-quality after-photographs of our cosmetic cases and send the patient a copy. It's a service that they don't get from most dental offices. Imagine what they say when someone sees this photograph in their home and comments on how nice it looks. *'My dentist took that picture after he did some work on me.'* Can you imagine someone <u>not</u> being impressed? Patients tell me they saw someone's picture and wanted work just like theirs."

"That's a great idea!" said Dr. Triet, excitedly.

"It works." said Will. "It's little things like this that separate you from the average practice and let you develop the practice I know you all want."

"What's that room for?" asked Fonda, pointing to a door on which the words 'Junior Staff Member Room' were painted.

"It's where the joy of my life -- my little boy -- and my staff's kids are watched during the day," said Will, beaming. "Just being able to walk in and see him can make even the worst day and its problems melt away. I love having him here. We hired a recently retired patient to watch them. She's terrific. They all call her grandma. Understand, this is not for patients' children, which could be a legal nightmare. You are not running a baby-sitting service and our patients know that their children are not allowed back here."

"What a great idea," said Fonda. "I bet your staff loves this."

"Sure," said Will. "I provide the facility, and we all share the cost of the service. You can work it out in lieu of a bonus or raise, or have them pay a portion, depending on the number of kids they have. Although it was not conceived as an image builder, it hasn't hurt me with the mothers in the practice. They think I'm wonderful for doing this."

"I sure do!" said Fonda.

"Speaking of my little boy, I need to get home, " said Will. "I promised my wife I would watch him while she ran some errands. Actually, I look forward to these times alone together. Enjoy them while you can, 'cause they grow up way too fast. It won't be long till he's older and won't want me around like he does now."

The group followed Will toward the front of the office. Most of them looked around with great curiosity at the details -- nooks in the wall which held statues, architectural details in the ceiling -- but all of them stopped in amazement at the aviary which *all* the operatories faced and in the middle of which was a waterfall. The birds were playing in the waterfall as if they were taking a bath.

"Incredible," said Fonda.

They walked by the radiograph center where a panographic x-ray, conventional x-ray machine and a digital radiography monitor and sensor were housed. Even that room appeared friendly. Dr. Excel gave them a brief demonstration of the ability of the digital equipment, and printed out a hard copy of an existing saved image.

They walked to the front door.

"Dr. Excel, we all want to thank you for sharing your day with us and giving us so much of your time and help," said Evan.

"No problem," said Will. "I've been blessed, and I want to share my good fortunes with others. You know, you guys are not my competition. There is enough work for all of us, if you would only diagnose it. If our profession can make dentistry a desirable commodity, we all would be busier than we would ever desire.

"One more thing before you go: Remember, it's not a crime to be successful. Our profession has inadvertently promoted that feeling amongst its members, and it's wrong. Think of who you admire. The successful people. The sooner you come to terms with that philosophy, the sooner you can become a success. Good-bye, for now."

The group left Will's office, thinking about his last words. Most of them realized they hid their success from their patients, and that they felt guilty about that success. They realized what he said was right and decided independently that it would be okay if they became more successful.

Chapter Twelve

Competition
How To Charge More When Everyone Else Is Charging Less

The phone rang. Will picked it right up so as not to wake his sleeping son.

"Hello."

"Hi, Will," said Evan. He sounded dejected. "How are you doing today?"

"Great!" said Will. "I had a lot of fun in the office today."

"That's good," said Evan, somewhat distracted. "I need your advice, have you got some time?"

"Sure, Evan. You sound dejected. What can I do for you?"

"I am trying to implement your principles, but I can't do it at the fees the rest of the dentists in town charge," said Evan. "I want a practice like yours so much, but I'm afraid if I raise my fees, my patients will go to the guys down the street who charge less. I know you told us that it won't happen, but it's hard to compete with them."

Will took a deep breath.

"You know that dental fees are a pet peeve of mine," said Will. "The fact that they have not kept up with inflation for 20 years is pretty disgusting. It may be illegal to be crooked, but it's not illegal to be stupid. I just read a book by Lawrence Steinmetz called, "How to Sell at Prices Higher Than Your Competitors." He says that no one has ever called the Mafia poor business people.

"It's not the crooked dentist who is ruining the profession -- the law and the patients will take care of them -- it's the dentist who doesn't know about business who is destroying it. You can't compete with someone who is giving away their the services. As the great philosopher *Pogo* said, *'We have found the enemy and he is us.'* If, however, your prices go down, it's a self-inflicted wound.

"Most dentists think that success is a by-product of volume. Business is not a game of volume, but a game of margins. I've known million dollar practices that have failed. Gone broke! Their comment was, 'We were busy up 'til the last day.' If your overhead is too close to your collections, who cares what the figure is!"

"Evan, you can't compete with the low fee dentists, because if they can sell at those prices and **not** prosper, so can you. Since you *can't* compete, ***don't***. Use service as a marketing edge. They can't provide the service you can because they will only go under *faster*. It is so easy to market service, because most dentists won't.

"If you are going to err in your fees, err on the high side. It's always easier to lower your price than to raise it. Besides, if you *underprice*, you fail working your buns off whereas if you **overprice** and fail, at least your health is better. I would rather <u>not</u>

be busy and <u>not</u> make anything than work hard and not make anything. Wouldn't you?"

"Of course," said Evan. "But..."

"No buts," snapped Will. "If I'm not busy then I can then concentrate on the people who appreciate quality. Then you build your practice with quality-conscious patients. Besides, my # 1 rule is: *If no one complains about your price, you're charging too little.* My #2 rule is: *Never let the dumbest guy in town set your prices."*

"Well, that makes sense," said Evan, laughing.

"Price is never the cause for production decline -- service is the problem," said Will. "Patients will pay extra if they believe they are getting what they pay for. If your service is commensurate with your fees, they will gladly pay them. Most people do not use price as their deciding factor."

"They seem to use price as a deciding factor in my practice!" said Evan.

"The only reason they tell you they buy on price is to get you to cut yours," said Will. "If price is the only factor, why do people pay extra for the same gas at a gas station to use their credit card? Convenience. If price were the only factor, there would be no Nordstroms, Lexus, or Rolex."

"That's true," said Evan. "So what you're saying is..."

"What I'm saying is that you will **prosper** providing a low-volume, high-quality care. You will enjoy dentistry more, feel better about your work and be able to sleep better at night. The key is to just charge what you are worth. In fact, charge *more* than you are worth, and you will become worth what you charge. When you stop thinking about money and do the right thing, the money comes pouring in. Trust me, it's true. It happened to me."

"I know, but maybe it's just because it's you," said Evan. "Maybe it's because you're a better dentist. I think I need to get a lot more patients so I can have more to choose from before I make these changes."

Will laughed and then said, "Ralph Waldo Emerson said '*He who has a better mouse trap will find the world will beat a path to his door.*' Well guess what, he was wrong, and in fact he was not successful. He had no money and lived like a recluse. You show me a beaten path to a door and

I'll show you someone who's charging too little. You don't want a beaten path. You don't want to work that hard, or you won't enjoy what you are doing. Cater to a select few who appreciate what you are doing and success will be yours.

"I prefer the following quote: *'It's unwise to pay too much, but it's worse to pay too little. When you pay too much, you lose a little money....that's all. When you pay too little, you sometimes lose everything, because the thing you bought was incapable of doing the thing you bought it to do. The common law of business balance prohibits paying a little and getting a lot... it can't be done.'*

"Who said that?" asked Evan.

"John Ruskin, and in the 19th century."

"That's well and good, Will, but how do you handle the price objection?" asked Evan.

"Your high price makes a statement, Evan, use it to your advantage," declared Will. "Let me share with you a few closes we use in our office to handle those situations:

"The **'Feel, Felt, Found'** close, in which we say, 'I understand how you feel, others have felt that way. However, they found that the treatment they received was well worth the price. Why do you think so many others buy our services at that price?'

"The **'Quality Requirement Close,'** in which we say, 'You know, we are so busy now, we are afraid of our quality suffering if we lower our prices. We want to make sure we have enough time to spend with those that really appreciate quality.'

"The **'Conditioned Loss Close,'** in which we say 'Sure, we *may* have lost a few patients because of our price, but we have *never* lost a patient because they were dissatisfied with our work.'

"Wow," said Evan. "Those are great. Why didn't I think of them?"

"You can and you will," said Will. "It is so easy to use high price as a marketing tool. Just use your imagination and work on it."

Thanks so much," said Evan elated. "You have made such a difference in my life and I want you to know that."

"And you, in mine," said Will. "Being able to help guys like you has enriched my life. I don't think you will ever know how much. Please, just spread the word, and help others who were like you, so we can save our profession from the negative influences that are trying to ruin it. Dentistry has given me a lot, as it has you, and we owe it to the profession to help save it for the next generation.

"I promise," said Evan. "I will."

Evan hung up with a commitment to uphold his promise and teach others how to be successful.

Epilogue

It had been more than ten years since Dr. Plateau had that last conversation with Dr. Excel. They had spoken several times over the years, but as Evan looked across the room of mourners dressed in black, he regretted the long gaps between each talk.

During the eulogy he thought about all Will had done for him and others like him. It was because of *him* that Evan had gone on to teach *other* dentists about the good things available in dentistry and how they can enjoy the profession more than *most* think is possible.

He noticed Dr. Excel's handsome son in the front, and marveled at how he had grown into a fine boy. It seemed he was barely a teenager. He was saddened to think that Dr. Excel was much to young to have left his son without a father. The loss, too was felt by other dentists he inspired and guided, but Evan thought that the loss must be unbelievably hard for the child.

"I would like to quote one of Will's favorite lines," said Dr. Excel's partner as he addressed the crowd. "It's from Helen Keller and he had used it often. *'Security is mostly a superstition. It does not exist in nature....life is either a daring adventure or nothing.'* There is no doubt that Will lived this philosophy to the fullest. Those of you who knew Will as a colleague, lecturer, or respected clinician, have been touched by his inspiration. Not only did he bring happiness and rewards to you, but to those around you, who *you* influenced by *his* example."

Evan thought about how Will had changed *his* life. He had adopted this philosophy as well and lived life as a daring adventure. He looked around at the glistening eyes in the room and noticed the others who had been inspired by his example and had found the riches in life because of him. Dentists who had both sought his inspirational message and been treated by him themselves were present.

Evan remembered the kind of dentist he had been before he was influenced by Dr. Excel and remembered another of his favorite quotes that affected him back then:

'You cannot discover new oceans unless you have the courage to lose site of the shore.'

Evan, as well as these others, had learned to enjoy dentistry more and work smarter -- not harder -- because of his philosophies. He knew that it was his duty to perpetuate the message and inspire as many dentists as possible.

As they were leaving the service, Evan walked over to Will's young son.

"Your dad changed my life and I will forever be grateful," said Evan.

"Thank you, sir," said the young man. "He was an inspiration to me as well. I miss him very much."

Evan noticed the swollen red eyes and knew the loss was a deep one. He remembered how much Will had thought of the child and how he always rushed home to spend some time together. It bothered Evan that he was responsible for some of their time apart. The sacrifices Dr. Excel had made were indeed costly ones, thought Evan.

"I'm sorry about the loss of your dad, and I'm really sorry that I took him away from you on those occasions I needed his help," said Evan. "If there is anything I can ever do for you, please let me know." Evan put his arm around the boy's shoulder.

"Don't be sorry, sir," the young boy responded. "It was what he enjoyed and it set a great example for me to follow. My Dad felt alive and was happy because of what he did for you and others like you. I wouldn't have traded my Dad's happiness for all the time in the world with him. I do, however, appreciate your thoughts."

Evan marveled how mature this young man was and how Will had done a marvelous job raising him. He could tell he was proud of his father's accomplishments.

Evan realized that life is a balancing act between ones professional accomplishments and family responsibilities. He wondered which was more important, providing for them financially or providing emotional support? He knew that often *one* was forced to suffer because of the *other*. He realized how much he loved his own children and missed the times he was away from them. He also knew, however, that one's self worth is important and that the feeling of accomplishing is critical to one's self esteem.

Only when this inner peace is achieved, can you really be a proper guidance to your children, thought Evan.

Evan realized that much of the boy's guidance was directed by the father's feelings of self achievement.

Evan walked away with a mixed feeling of sadness and joy. The loss of his mentor was tragic, and yet he knew he would continue to be a gate-keeper and preach the message that Dr. Excel had taught him. And he would do it with more vigor than ever.

He also realized that life is both precious and short, and resolved to enjoy the really *important* things in life to the fullest.

"If one advances confidently in the direction of their dreams, and endeavors to lead a life which they have imagined, they will meet with a success unexpected in common hours."

Henry David Thoreau